FIVE STEPS

Meditative Sensation
Walking

Paul H. Crompton Ltd.
94 Felsham Road, London, SW15 1DQ.
England

First Edition 1999

Copyright © 1996 - Paul H. Crompton

ISBN 1 874250 60 X

Photo source: Digital Vision ©

*Printed and bound in England
by Caric Press, Clerwood, Corunna Main,
Andover, Hampshire,
SP10 1JE.
(01264) 354887*

You will find out what this book is about only by trying to do what it says.

If you have any health problems, you should consult a physician before doing the movements which are described in the book.

CONTENTS............................?

There
Are
No
"Subjects"
In
This
Book

Someone said:

Your brain was designed to be able to be clear and impartial. Your feelings were designed to be compassionate towards others and yourself.

Your body was designed both to live its own life and to serve your brain and feelings.

Someone wrote:

All men are brothers. And all the parts of a man, or woman, are brothers and sisters.

If these parts can learn to live as brothers and sisters then we may yet save ourselves from destruction.

FOREWORD

A large number of people in many countries have been reading my writings and watching video tapes produced by me for over thirty years. These have mainly been confined to the fields of martial arts, Tai Chi Chuan and Chi Kung. I have received many letters, faxes, phone calls and face to face messages thanking me for the beneficial effects these productions have given to people.

The subjects dealt with in the productions mentioned are mostly quite complex. The contents of this book are simple and straightforward. In my view, they are more accessible for people who do not want to become involved in intellectual and physical material that has no direct bearing on their immediate lives. At the same time, the effort needed to swim through this book is directly related to its simplicity.

In a "sea if troubles" it is sometimes hard to discriminate and find the essential, the simple. This book is a step in that direction I believe.

Relax
as you
walk

INTRODUCTION

We are trying to do something which really needs a teacher, live, on the spot. This means that to counterbalance the lack of direct tuition the reader or student must work harder than the writer, much harder. It also means that just as in a live lesson there is often much repetition, so in this book there is also some repetition.

The number of movements or actions to be learned are few. It is the way the actions are to be tried which are many. In other words the details of how you move, and what you are trying to do inside yourself, are many. This explains the sub-title of the book: Meditative Sensation Walking.

Meditation depends on focusing attention. In this book the attention is focused on the movement and sensation of the body. The nervous system is so constructed that a person can move without any awareness of the body at all. In fact that is how most of us move. Fortunately, for us, the whole body operates without our needing to direct it. If it needed our full time cooperation we would have died soon after birth. The book will not foolishly call upon the reader to regulate or re-order any vital processes of the body, but rather aim to cultivate awareness of the "alive" of the body, through directing attention to the sensations which that "alive" produces.

Chapter 1

A simple method runs through the book. This method is used to cultivate the relationship between attention, movement and the body sensation referred to. The method is to study and move at the same time. A balance is kept between the two. You always try to move with awareness of what you are doing. What does this mean? The question cannot be answered here, because the whole of the book is about just that question.

Experience with a wide range of people of all ages and from a wide range of occupations has convinced me of the truth of the assertion that we are not aware of our bodies when we move about, or when we are sitting down.

The body is producing "messages" which we could be aware of but it is as though we were switched off. It is as simple as a radio. The messages are there but you have to switch on the radio to hear them. So we can say that meditative sensation walking is about switching on the inside radio. There is a major difference though. When we listen to the radio we cannot change what is being said or played on it. But if we learn to pay attention we can influence what the body is saying or playing to us. We can learn to "micro" adjust the body's position, its joint use, its relaxation, and through this to even find a new attitude and feeling towards it and inside it.

Millions of people were thrilled and touched by a programme which showed an American "cowboy" Monty Roberts break in a horse through mere body language. He did not lay a finger on it, initially, but merely communicated with it in a language it understood; a language which the cowboy himself first had to learn. Simply by dropping and raising his head, by turning away from the animal or looking at it he was able to befriend it and gain its trust. There is a direct analogy here between the possible relationship between our psyche and our organic body.

The link between them is our attention.

When Sun Lu-tang, an eminent Chinese martial arts teacher, was close to death, his disciples were eager to know if he had any last "secrets" to pass on to them before he died. On his death bed, so the account goes, they asked him about his "secrets". He picked up his brush and wrote one character:

"PRACTISE".

Illustrations of the Five Steps keep appearing in the book. This is so that you have them before you as you are reading. You do not have to keep turning back to look at them. And though the illustrations are the same, it is hoped that what you "see" as you work through the suggestions will change. You will not see the same photographs because you will see them through the eyes of growing experience of what those movements contain. It is like a dancer or a martial artist or an ice skater looking at photographs of his art. When he starts to learn he will see just a picture. After a few months he will see the same picture but he begins to know what it is going on in that picture. After a couple of years he will be able to look at such a picture and "see" a lot. He has been there himself, more than once, and he knows what he is looking at.

It is important not to jump pages, and not to rush. If you do this you will miss something and this will not help. As the weeks and months roll by, if you continue, you will slowly acquire a language of movement and sensation which you will be able to "speak". Already you have a language of recognition of tastes and smells, non-verbal at the initial moment of recognition. Similarly a growing non-verbal language of movement sensation can be yours with sufficient application and effort.

During this process you will have learned the Five Steps. They are nothing more than an excellent framework within which the new language can be learned. Once you begin to be familiar with it you will see that it can be spoken during daily life and not just during the Five Steps.

From time to time there are some little "asides" in the book which hopefully will produce some "moods" which may be helpful. Like this.

ASIDE

When I was a teenager I was often unhappy, as teenagers often are. During these years I wondered about things like, What is religion all about, What is the meaning of life, What was I meant to do with my life on earth? School friends and I talked at great length about such subjects. We argued, and from my point of view we got nowhere. I talked to members of the family, with Christian priests, monks, Hindu swamis and all manner of people. I discovered books with exercises on "meditation", yoga, devotional mystical writings, and so on but to no lasting avail. From time to time it did seem to me that I saw light, and everything was clear. But then the clarity disappeared leaving me once more in the dark.

Several years passed, and then it began to dawn on me that my difficulty took on a particular form. What happened was that I intermittently built up an explanation or view of how things were, based on the ideas and feelings I had at the time. I then felt reassured and clear because I had a clear "picture". I was taking comfort from an image; it was a kind of psychological raft on which to float through the sea of life. But then something would happen; a change of mood or circumstances, a change of thoughts and feelings. In any case, whatever the cause, a change happened and this usually signalled that I was back in the water, floundering, unhappy. My raft had broken up and sunk. This is not an uncommon experience but I did not know this then, and besides, it was happening to me!

Decades later I can look back at the young fellow that I was and see my fundamental misunderstanding at the time. One of the things I was in error about was to cling to what was no more than a personal picture or construction of what my life was about. It had no real foundation. It was built on psychological sand. What I needed was to see that life changes, all the time, and I lacked the understanding and experience to see this clearly. I would have been better served if I could have found someone who could show me how to swim, rather than build my own raft and hold on to it.

Partly I suppose I was one of many victims of an educational system which teaches the importance of learning many so-called facts, at the expense of direct perception; and teaches also the reliance on those facts in circumstances which are inappropriate.

Early in my own life I was fortunate to discover people who had not only perceived the reality of this situation but who had found certain remedies for it. This book is an attempt to pass on part of the message I received from others, and also to discharge a certain obligation which I feel towards those who helped me at a crucial time in my life.

One important aspect of this guidance was to bring into focus what I have already stressed: that we are not aware of ourselves. Not that we do not think about ourselves or that we cannot look introspectively into ourselves, but that we are not directly aware; aware without the misleading screen of thought processes, judgements and reactions.

This does not mean that thoughts and reactions are wrong. The preoccupations of the day are real and necessary. But if we are never directly aware of ourselves then some parts of us are in fact starving. It is like a mother with three children, who favours one and neglects the other two. A first step in beginning to understand and remedy this situation is to begin to become aware of the body, my body; that it exists, that it is important, and that although it does not directly take part in my thoughts and plans it is the place in which I live. It is one of the family!

To begin to pay it attention will be like the mother giving attention to a child she has neglected. How welcome it will be! It will be like the prodigal son returning to the attention of his father. If the mother can learn to distribute her attention among her three children more or less equally, this will tend to produce a harmonious family.

It takes time and regular study, and patience, another neglected child.

Chapter 2

WORDS 1

1. Stand up straight as in fig. 1.
2. Look horizontally ahead into the middle distance without staring.
3. Put the heel of your right foot on the floor as in fig. 2.
4. Bend the knee of your left leg and lower your right sole to the floor as in fig. 3.
5. Shift the weight of the body on to the right foot, bending the knee a little, and raising the heel of the left foot as in fig. 4.

DO THESE MOVEMENTS ANY WAY YOU CAN, FIRST WITH LEFT FOOT LEADING AND THEN RIGHT FOOT LEADING, ABOUT A DOZEN TIMES.

1

2

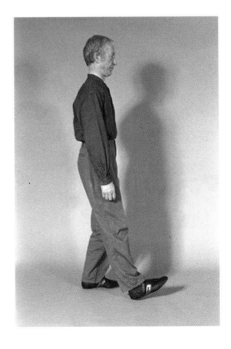

3

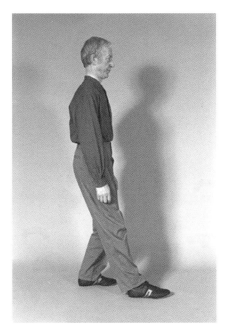

4

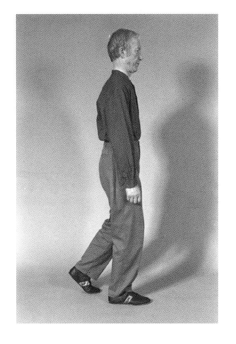

MEDITATION?

Meditation is a common expression these days. It is a media-happy word. Everyone "knows" what it means. What does it mean? One expert on the origins of English words explains that it has to do at its root with paying attention. If this is so, we can see that over the course of time this fact has been overlooked. Instead, the things or acts towards which attention has been directed have taken pride of place. For example, the sort of acts referred to are:

watching breathing and counting breaths

staring at an object such as a candle

repeating a word (mantra)

The primary capacity which makes these acts possible - attention - is largely forgotten. It is not so much what is given attention, but the giving of attention which comes first. By giving attention to the body, your body, you will be both cultivating attention-giving and bringing into the family circle an important, indeed essential member. This member, the body, is what helps us to have the energy for attention in the first place.

WORDS 2

Repeat the movements following the instructions given so far.
1. Stand up straight.
2. Stay still and relax as much as you can for about thirty seconds.
3. Place the left heel on the floor, and then using the muscle which lies along the outside of the left shin bone you pull the foot gently up towards the shin. That is, you contract your ankle joint with the help of the muscle, fig. 1.
4. Bend your right knee slowly and lower the sole of the left foot to the ground.
5. Shift your weight on to the left foot and raise the heel of the right foot.

REPEAT WITH THE RIGHT FOOT,
AND CONTINUE FOR ABOUT A
DOZEN TIMES. STAY SIMPLE.

Keep right knee bent and gently pull on the muscles on the side of shin...

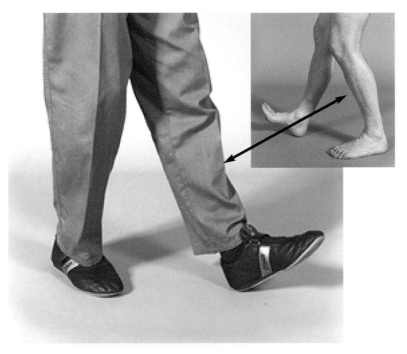

ASIDE

Sometimes you are sitting, waiting for something to happen. A friend is coming, a train is coming, or you are waiting in a queue for something. Nothing, it seems, is happening. You don't want to read a magazine, listen to the radio, watch television or talk to anyone. You have time on your hands. You are not exactly bored, nor are you interested. What you see and hear around you has no particular interest for you. How would you describe the way you are at that moment?

You could say that there is a new possibility which you are ignoring, because you are not really awake to it. You are there, but *you* are not there. If you focus a little, as with a camera lens, you may become aware of the presence of your own attention; attention which, for once, is not absorbed by anything in particular.

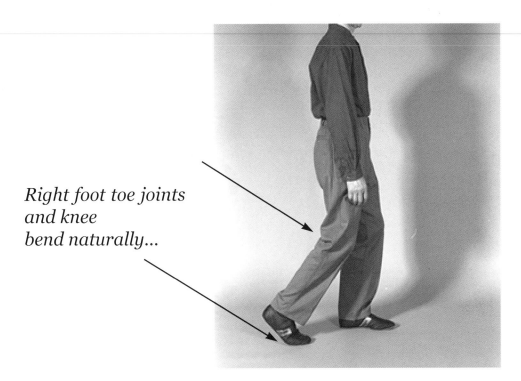

*Right foot toe joints
and knee
bend naturally...*

WORDS 3

Be sure you remember the instructions in Words 2 and can carry them out.

1. Stand up straight.
2. Focus on relaxing the muscles of your face for about a minute. Remove unnecessary facial expressions.
3. Left heel on the floor. Gently contract the muscles on the front of the left thigh.
4. Bend the right knee slowly and lower the sole of the left foot to the floor, relaxing the thigh muscles, the shin muscles, the ankle and knee joints.
5. Shift your weight on to the left foot, slowly, and raise the heel of the right foot.

FOCUS ON THESE ALTERNATING RELAXING AND CONTRACTING POINTS UNTIL YOU CAN PRODUCE SOME APPRECIABLE CHANGES IN THE TONE OR TENSION-STATE OF THOSE MUSCLES.

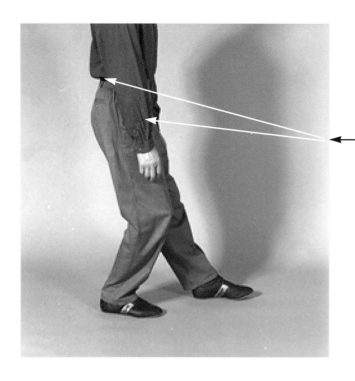

Sometimes tuck in at the groin, with an accompanying "yawn-like" lower back stretch - small but appreciable.

WORDS 4

1. Stand up straight.
2. Focus for about a minute on relaxing the muscles of your shoulders and arms.
3. Left heel on the floor. As you gently contract the required muscles of the left leg, focus on your face and shoulders to make sure that the contraction in the leg does not produce a contraction elsewhere which is not required.
4. Bend the right knee, lower the left sole to the floor. Occasionally, when you reach this movement, push your buttocks back a few inches to make a deeper bend at the groin-hip. As you do so, let the muscles of the lower back stretch comfortably.
5. Finish the sequence and repeat on both legs about a dozen times.

AS YOU MOVE, BE CURIOUS ABOUT THE CHANGES IN SENSATION WHICH OCCUR.

*A*SIDE

We often hear someone say they have no spare time. One of my first teachers was familar with that plea. She used to say that when people are in love they always find time for sex. There is some truth in that.

Relax
as you
walk

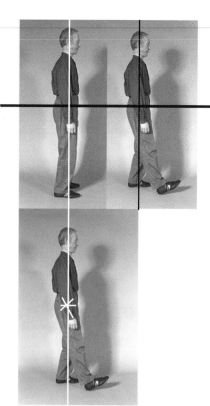

Centre of gravity does not
move forward
as you put your foot down

Words 5

The distance at which you place your foot in front of you when taking the first step is very important and up to now has been left to you. It is governed by a simple factor, and is one of the most important points in this book. When you lift your right foot and place it down, your trunk should not move forward.

Body weight is centred over the left foot and the right foot moves into place without disturbing that centre of gravity. This factor determines the distance forward that you place your left foot. Make this determining of the correct distance the main thing now as you go through the steps. As it is the first move you make it needs to be right. If you cannot be sure of your position, get a mirror, put a piece of paper or mark on the mirror opposite a place on your trunk, take your step and make sure the point on your body and the mark on the mirror stay in line. You sink but you do not move forwards. A number of traditional teachings contain physical movements which are simple. The simplicity of the movements make the directing of attention to other, specific, elements more possible.

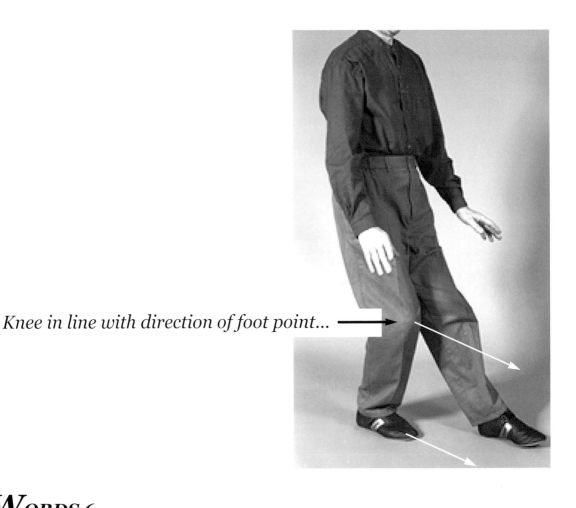

Knee in line with direction of foot point... →

Words 6

1. Stand up straight and focus on relaxing the muscles of your wrists, palms and fingers.
2. Left heel on the floor.
3. As you proceed to lower your left sole, focus on the right knee, visually, and make sure it is in line with or over the right foot. Do not let your right knee bend inwards or outwards above the ankle joint so that it is out of alignment. If you have a long standing mis-alignment at the ankle then do not force it straight. Try to correct it slowly. It may respond, or it may not.
4. Notice that as you shift your weight forward on to the left foot, you can be aware of the increased pressure upon it and the decrease in pressure on the right foot.

A_{SIDE}

Sometimes a person will say to you, "Just act naturally". I am wondering what this means. What does it mean to act naturally? It is probably true to say that in the natural world, animals and plants act naturally! Probably very young children also do.

But an older person is subject to many vagaries of mood and thought which cause him or her to act differently at any given moment. In these circumstances, what is it to act naturally?

Chapter 3

An important point about the beginning of the Five Steps has been left up to you so far, but now it needs to be clarified. It concerns the distance between your feet when you are standing up straight at the beginning. Your feet should be directly under your hips, or you could say the distance of your hips apart. Secondly, both feet should be pointing straight ahead, parallel to one another.

Then, as you step forward each time, you step along the line your foot is pointing along. It is as though your feet were moving along a narrow railway track, with a foot on each line.

Earlier, patience was mentioned. You may be a very patient person. If so, use your patience all the way through. Patience is hard to define but it does have something of persistence in it. It is one of our inner children. Feed it. No matter how much the other children clamour for attention, do not ignore patience. Clamourers have little or no patience, and can all benefit from the growth of their brother or sister patience. As it grows, relaxation will grow, and as relaxation grows, breathing will become more natural.

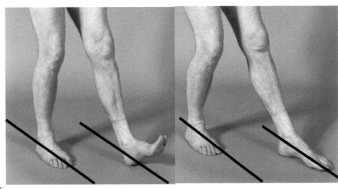

Walk on the railway lines with straight feet...

*W*ORDS 7

1.   Stand straight with feet the distance of the hips apart. Your gaze is focusing on nothing, but at the same time you "look" inside at the sensation and position of your body. The nervous system is sending messages to you about this and you look-listen.

2.   Relax the eyeballs and the muscles surrounding them.

3.   Take your first heel step and lower the sole to the ground. Relax your right hip, knee and ankle. Bend forward and slap your knee joint with your right hand, from behind. If it is relaxed, the knee joint will bend forward as you slap and fall back straightening itself, fig. 1. If you cannot do this at once, study how to let your leg relax until you can do it. Try grasping your knee cap with your fingertips; you should be able to move it freely around.

4.   Straighten up and continue with your movements. Occasionally train in stockinged or bare feet so that you can experience the support given by the arches rather than the support of your shoe.

SOMETIMES, PAUSE BETWEEN STEPS. *LISTEN* TO WHAT YOU ARE GOING TO DO *BEFORE* YOU DO IT. THEN SOMETIMES YOU MAY FIND A BETTER WAY OF MOVING.

Slap knee loosely from behind.
It should bend forwards and flop back.
If it doesn't, your knee is not sufficiently relaxed.

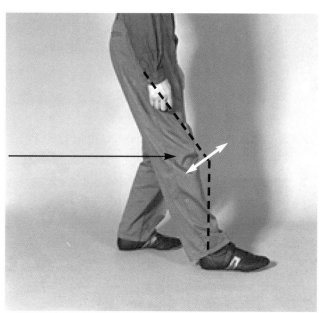

A FEW THOUGHTS

At the time I was plodding through the writing and rewriting of this book I read a book by Oliver Sacks, "An Anthropologist on Mars". Sacks has written a number of works about people with neurological disorders. These writings have been greatly admired and some have been the basis for films or theatrical productions. One of the chapters of the book is called "Prodigies" and deals with mainly autistic subjects with extraordinary powers of memory or manual dexterity. Sacks quotes from the writings of A.C. Aitken, "a great mathematician and calculator" (not autistic). Aitken wrote:

"I have noticed at times that the mind has anticipated the will; I have had an answer before I even wished to do the calculation; I have checked it, and am always surprised that it is correct. This, I suppose (but the terminology may not be right), is the subconscious in action at several levels; and I believe that each of these levels *has its own velocity* (italics author's), different from that of our ordinary waking time, in which our processes of thought are rather tardy."

This paragraph is relevant to what we are trying with our Five Steps. Aitken makes the point that what he calls the subconscious may work at a different velocity from what we call the conscious. This may explain why he experienced the working out of the calculation seemingly before he had decided to make it. But when he says the word "I", what or who does he mean?

An autistic person, as in the film "Rain Man", may exhibit a comparable capacity to that which Aitken described. Dustin Hoffman sees a box of matches fall to the floor of a diner and knows how many there are scattered around, at a single glance. He does not count them one at a time. He simply says aloud how many there are. How can we explain this? Maybe one part of his brain by-passes another, and much more quickly "counts". Or does it count at all? Does it just see 95, or 56, or 102, whatever the number is?

When I was at primary school (under age 11 years), our teacher would spring on us a mental arithmetic test in which he asked us to do a calculation without pen and paper (no calculators in those days). On one such occasion I spoke the answer almost before he had finished asking the question. He stared at me and said, "How did you do that?" I wanted to give him an explanation but could not. The calculation had been done before "I" could do it. This type of experience goes on all the time but we do not notice it. It illustrates that we have more than one "calculator" or "brain" and perhaps within each of these there are further sub-divisions where more specialised processes take place. The main thrust of our education and upbringing does not take this into account, but follows the belief that if we "know" something it must be through our ordinary, accepted mental processes.

But in attempting to study the simple movements of the Five Steps we are discovering that one of more of our neglected faculties can be of benefit to us if we pay more attention.

In trying to respond to the messages of body sensation a person can perceive habits of tension, habits of locking the joints for no good reason, and so forth. In doing so, he or she can learn to be sensitive to what is required to unlock them. If the person persists, and does not give up easily. then more and more things of this nature will become clearer. The comparison with the swift calculation examples is this. The swift, unconscious calculation can be compared with the intrinsic knowledge the body has of its own movement capacities. The slow calculation can be compared with the usual ways of moving and body-awareness a person has. We are trying to make friends with the intrinsic faculties of the body.

WORDS 8

1.   Stand straight. Imagine that you relax the roots of your hair and scalp muscles. Let this relaxation flow from the top of your head like water from a shower, over your face and neck and down over your whole body; to your finger tips and toe tips.

2.   As an experiment, place your hands on your hips. As you raise your left foot and place your heel on the floor, notice that your hips/pelvis move over to the right as the centre of gravity moves sideways. Do not let your pelvis move forwards.

3.   As you shift weight forwards on to the left foot let your arms hang down heavily with their own weight. At the same time, think of your head floating up from your spine fig. 1.

4.   Continue with the movements about a dozen times.

Do not want to move forward and do not want to stand still!

?

?

Do both...

Note: By this time you will surely have noticed that a lot of your muscular tensions and postures come from psychological causes. A good example is your attitude towards moving forwards. When you are standing up straight, before you move, ask yourself if you "want" to move. If you want to move, you are marginally too tense for what we want. Try to find an attitude which is indifferent to whether you move or remain still. Do not move and do not stay still.

Chapter 4

WORDS 9

1.   Stand up straight. Relax your chest and abdomen by letting go. Whether you can or not does not matter at this stage. You simply think of letting them go whilst being aware of them. At this stage, you will be standing still for some time, going over the relaxation suggestions made so far. With time and training your "list" will become a kind of "scan" which is less stilted than at first.
2.   Lift the right leg and place the heel.
3.   Lower the sole to the ground and this time emphasise relaxing your buttocks.
4.   Shift weight on to the right foot, raising the left heel. On this occasion, as an experiment again, shift weight back on to the left foot, raising the toes of the right foot, then forward on to the right foot, several times. Note - during this try out, notice the changes in the feet and legs composition.

Note: Walking in the way described needs space. You may have to adopt the device of walking in a circular or elliptical direction. If this is not feasible for you, then walk forwards then backwards, as described in the next section.

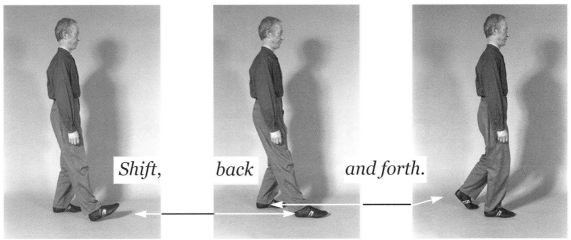

Shift,   *back*   *and forth.*

WORDS 10

At this tenth phase try walking backwards.

1. Stand in the usual preparatory position.
2. Lift the right leg and place the ball of the foot directly behind you, fig. 1.
3. Shift the weight on to the right foot, keeping the sole of the left foot on the ground fig. 2.
4. Straighten the right knee a little and raise the left sole, flexing the ankle upwards towards the shin, fig. 3.
5. Continue backwards with the left foot.

UNCERTAINTY WHEN MOVING BACKWARDS PRODUCES TENSIONS BUT YOU WILL SOON GET OVER THIS.

Note: every "technical" instruction word is significant. Do not leave anything out.

1   2   3   *continue.....*

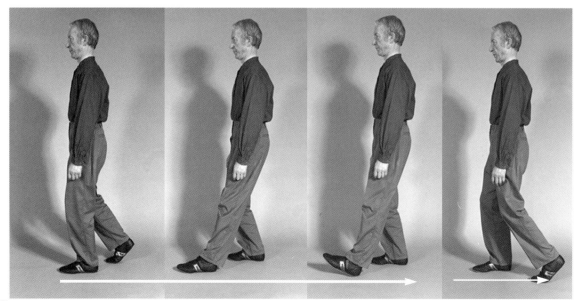

*W*ORDS 11

Still backwards...

1.   Stand as in fig. 1 and prepare not to move the centre of gravity backwards. Keep the weight over the foot which does not move.
2.   Move the right leg back only so far as not to shift the centre of gravity fig. 2.
3.   Shift weight backwards on to the right foot and let the weight spread comfortably, settling on the foot. Keep the sole of the left foot on the ground with a relaxed leg. Shift back and forth to experience the transition, figs. 2 and 3.
4.   Continue as in the previous section.

IF YOU HAVE PATIENCE, GO THROUGH THE WALKING BACKWARDS GRADUALLY, USING EVERYTHING YOU DID IN THE WALKING FORWARDS SECTION.

1   2   3

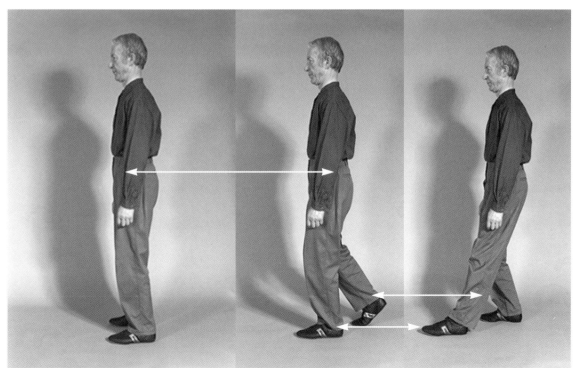

Chapter 5

If you have been doing what this book suggests for some time, you will have had by now a wealth of new experience about yourself and how you do move, and how you can move, and what the effects can be. Where does this new data belong? It does not belong in the part of you where you remember your telephone numbers, or how much money you have in the bank, or what your overdraft is, and so forth. It is new experience, coming from physical movements which prevent you from moving as you usually do. It requires cooperation from different parts of yourself and they all have to remember what to do. It is wheels meeting wheels.

TWO NEW MOVEMENTS

To complete the Five Steps we need two more movements. They call into play muscles which have not been used much so far. In doing so they expand the area of awareness in the sense of giving us more obvious experience of those muscles.

These movements also bring into focus the subject of breathing. This is a subject which benefits from little being said about it. It is a natural process and in normally functioning bodies would adapt itself harmoniously with each movement we make. This does not take place very frequently except perhaps when we are asleep in bed, working manually hard, or for some reason feeling quite at ease.

 1    2    3

WORDS 12

First time through do the movements any way you can.

1. Stand straight as in fig. 1.
2. Make movement fig. 2.
3. Make movement fig. 3.
4. Move into fig. 4.
5. Straighten up into fig. 5.
6. Lift the knee as in fig. 6.
7. Place heel down and repeat using the other leg.

4

5

6

7

WORDS 13

1. Stand straight and go through as many of the previous preparatory relaxation exercises as you can remember or have patience to try.
2. Continue with the Five Steps you do already, putting the left heel to the floor then lowering the sole to the floor.
3. Push slowly forward from the right foot, keeping the sole of the right foot on the floor. Keep alignment of your trunk and head, bending the left knee. Do not let the bend in the left knee carry the knee-cap beyond the toes of the left foot, fig. 1.
3. Begin to straighten up, letting the right heel rise simply off the floor. Your body "swings" slowly upright, like a Japanese doll or foot-weighted toy with a hemi-spherical base fig. 2.
4. Raise the right thigh to a horizontal position letting the ankle relax downward, fig. 3.
5. Lower the right heel to the ground and continue.

THE INCLINATION OF THE BODY FORWARDS IS A BIG CHANGE. STUDY IT WITH YOUR ATTENTION AND AWARENESS. LET YOUR BODY TELL YOU WHAT IS HAPPENING.

1

2

*A*SIDE

When I was a boy we lived in a house which faced west. There was a small upstairs room. We called it the box room. I suppose it was a type of store room, as we had no attic. One fateful December I discovered that Father Christmas kept his toys there.

Sometimes I would go into the box room and look out at the sunsets. I don't recall exactly why, but when I did so I used to either watch the sunset itself or the light on the wall from the setting sun. I do recall that I seemed to be thinking about nothing; just looking; an experience without words. It was what some people call "just being there". Attention was at rest in me, and I experienced stillness and silence.

This must happen to everyone from time to time. But perhaps because the experience just comes upon us, just happens, we do not reflect on it, we do not give it much value. Yet it is one of the most important things that can take place in us. It shows that attention can be at rest, that we can be still. If this part of ourselves can be found, then why do we not find out how to visit it more often?

3

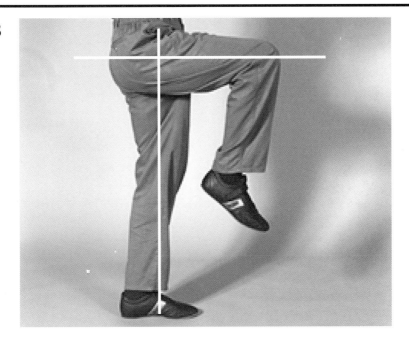

Relax as you walk

WORDS 14

1.   When you move into fig. 1 make sure there is no bending at the hip, lower back, middle of the back, or neck. In other words, the position of the body, from coccyx to fontanel, is as close to the alignment of the standing up position as possible. This may take some time to get right, so to begin with you settle for an approximation.

Stay in this position for a moment and touch the areas of potential bend in your trunk to manually find out what they are doing. A mirror might be useful too at this stage. Eventually you will be able to tell from your sensations if you are in the right position.

2.   Let the heel come up, relaxing the leg and allowing it to bend at the knee so the body swings up slowly to 2.

3.   This time, pause for a moment, then raise the knee to the horizontal. Later, do not make the pause, but move continuously.

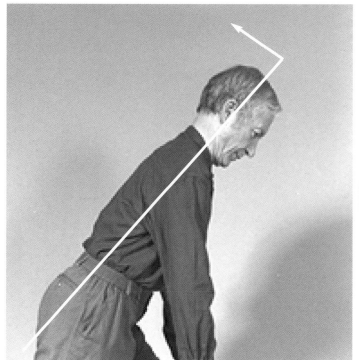

1

2

WORDS 15

1.   Go through to the position of being inclined forward. Pause again here and experiment with straightening the rear leg to a locked position, knee straight, then let it slacken, then lock. Notice also the possibilities of locking and slackening the hip and ankle joints. When you do the Five Steps as a regular thing, do not lock joints, that is, do not straighten them to their limit.

Put the palms of your hands on the back of your pelvis, and go through the locking and slackening of the joints again, noting the effects this has on the pelvis. Then further, try putting your hands on your pelvis and keeping it still as you flex and relax the joint muscles.

(right leg has been shown instead of left)

2.   Move into the vertical straightening and experience the "bobbing up" effect, fig. 1.

3.   Raise the left knee-thigh parallel with the floor and pause for a moment, fig. 2. Stabilise your body and try not to wobble or waver. In this position you can experiment with drawing yourself up straight to have the sensation of straightening your lower back. Then let yourself sink a few inches to let the back free. Continue with the other leg.

JOINTS HAVE PLAY IN THEM.   RELAXATION MAKES THIS CLEARER. ONCE YOU HAVE FOUND JOINT   RELAXATION, EXPERIMENT MOVING ANY JOINT INTO A SLOW, EASY FLEXED POSITION AND THEN SLOWLY LET IT GO. APPRECIATE THIS.

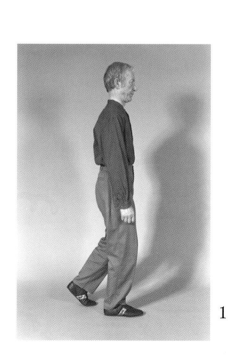

1

2

WORDS 16

1. Stand upright, becoming particularly aware of your arms, shoulders and chest muscles.
2. Raise the right leg and place the heel down.
3. Lower the right sole, bend the knee and then incline forwards in one single movement. Do this leaning with a feeling of assurance but not with haste.
4. Pause for a moment and allow your arms to hang heavily down. Let your pectorals (breast muscles) relax. They have no work to do in this position so let them briefly rest. Give this plenty of attention. Touch your pectorals and find how flaccid they can become. Fig. 1.

Have a break then try again. This time be aware of your shoulder blades, touch them with the back of one hand and find how they slide across your back when you let go of your arms. The many tendons and muscles attached to the shoulder blades will also tend to relax as you let the blades go. See clearly that in the inclined position the back does all the supporting work, together with the legs, and the front can really let go.

5. Swing up into the vertical, letting your arms and shoulder blades settle back into the new position required by standing up straight. Experience shows that most people have to learn to let the arms and shoulders go back, relying only on the pull of gravity. Initially, people tend either to hold their arms or "put" them back. Study how to let them move back on their own. Continue with the exercise.

BREATHING CAN CHANGE SPONTANEOUSLY EASILY IF THE LEANING FORWARDS IS DONE WELL. LET IT, DON'T COMPEL IT.

This completes the major section of the Five Steps which is concerned with stepping. Next we move on to the only arm movements it has.

Let arms hang down relaxed...

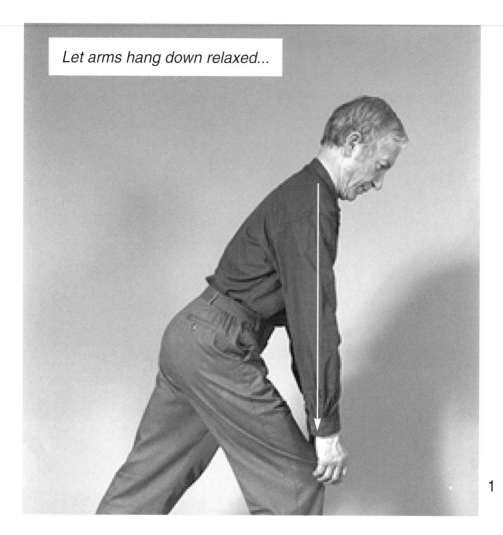

1

As you straighten up...

*relax and
let arms
and shoulders
slip back into
a gravity
hanging
position.*

SMALL THINGS

If you have got this far, and carried out even half of the suggestions made you will have begun to appreciate small things. That is, you will have become sensitive to adjustments of the body, and sensations of the body which you do not generally notice. This is what could be called an appreciative "taste". If you have not, this does not mean that the Five Steps are useless for you, but it does mean that they are not likely to be as helpful as they might be. If you think about it, this may clarify things.

For instance, the nervous system itself functions by being "self aware" in the sense that it is sensitive both to itself and the impact which the rest of the body makes upon it. This happens in the nervous system of someone who is fast asleep in bed, so we do not have to be awake in the ordinary sense for its self awareness to operate. All we have to do is to "tune in"; a hackneyed but nevertheless very apt expression. It is simple and directly to the point.

Pay attention to the "messages" of the living body.

ASIDE

As a teenager I went to France for a study holiday at a French school, along with other English teenagers. I made friends with another boy there. It happened that we both liked a girl who was on the course. On the final evening there was a dance and party in the school grounds. My new friend and I were walking along when I spotted a small wallet on the ground. I picked it up. It was fastened shut and there was no means of knowing whose it was. So I opened it.

There was a name inside. It was the girl's name. My friend was outraged. I had opened *her* wallet without *her* permission. It was not on, it was an insult to her... He shouted angrily at me from close range. It was not just the transgression against accepted behaviour but it was a transgression against the object of both of our affections!

Time stood still. I did not react. I was not intimidated, angry or ashamed of myself. I just looked at him with complete calm. After a few moments he lost his anger and stared at me, somehow sharing the state I found myself in. Both of us were at a loss to grasp what had taken place.

WORDS 18

1. Stand up straight.

2. Slowly raise your arms almost sideways but a little ahead of the shoulders, slowly, then lower them.

3. Do this a few times. Do it any way you wish and just be aware of the new movements.

The introduction of an arm movement is a major event. It means that the muscles which affect the chest come into play much more. In terms of the compass of our awareness, awareness is expanded. Raising the arms can be studied to begin with without any of the previous moves, as a preliminary. It is up to you to decide when to combine them with the other moves. Do not forget to relax. There is no end to it.

WORDS 19

1. Move slowly from fig. 1 to fig. 4.

As the elbows rise, forearms and hands following, it is like cracking a whip, very, very slowly. As your arms approach the horizontal, the forearms rise higher than the elbows, letting the wrists and hands trail down, but not floppy.

At first you will use your muscles too much to bring all this about, but as you study the actions more you will see that it is the slow momentum of the elbows rising and descending which produces the action of the forearms and hands. So as the wrists and hands reach the highest point of their rise, the elbows are going down, and then sinking to the sides of the trunk.   It is important not to slow down or speed up your breathing. You are moving slowly but you do not want to compel breathing to be slow also. Try to leave it alone by putting attention into relaxing, sensing your body and making synchronisation correct.

As the elbows rise, forearms and hands following, it is like cracking a whip, very, very slowly. As your arms approach the horizontal, the forearms rise higher than the elbows, letting the wrists and hands trail down, but not floppy. Then as the forearms and elbows descend, the wrists and hands rise higher fig. 7 and fig. 8.

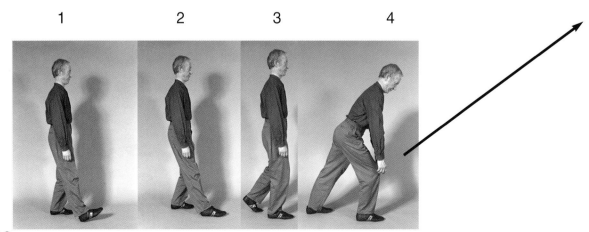

5

6

THE ACTION OF THE ARMS IS LIKE THE SLOW BEATING OF A BIRD'S WINGS. IMAGINE THAT YOU FLY THE THROUGH AIR, SENSING ITS PRESSSURE.

Continue to the end of the usual sequence.

7

8

THIS IS THE CONCLUSION OF DIRECT INSTRUCTIONS.

SONG OF THE FIVE STEPS

Upright on the magnet earth,
I stand with no trace of fear.

Patient, waiting, not hesitating,
I am simply, clearly, here.

Thoughts, ideas, translations
Cannot usurp this know.

Breathing in, breathing out,
I am touching, not in, the flow.

And there is no cause to make a move,
No cause to not make one;

Not from indecision, but here and now,
In the sphere of the life of the sun.

So move I do, just letting it work,
Taking part in what always goes on.

I do not wish to impose my will,
I do like a Father's son.

Sinking down, with just one knee,
And placing just one heel;

Gravity tells me how to be,
Yes, how to begin this meal.

There is no call, to think at all,

To taste is now my pleasure;

To taste sensation to the full,
With quite a different measure.

The left foot lowers, muscles give,
The right knee takes the weight.

Left speaks to right, right speaks to left,
Each to the other mate.

And all above can peaceful stand
Borne up and carried calm,

As forward lean continues through
Sensation like a charm.

And chest and arms can forward hang
Like servants taking ease;

Not uncognisant, duty-wise,
Just leaf-like in the breeze.

Leaf-like and like a leaf that moves
To soft-resistant air,

Not lazy shirking work a leaf
But simply taking share.

Now is the time to downward hang
And blood comes circling through.

Then trunk it upright swings and so
The arms rise up anew.

The leg goes with them, thigh bone lies
Horizontal to the earth,

And arm wings beat in tempo slow
And breath fills out to girth.

Floating like that gentle leaf
The arms and leg descend,

A touch of settle, moment's rest,
No dream that there is an end.

***

Body, body, speak to me,
Tell me what you know.

A million years you have toiled and tried
As the planet strove to grow.

From interstellar dust to slime
To mud, to earth and water,

Fire, air, all elements
Mixed true for son and daughter.

From father, mother, generations
Onwards body passed

Through tribes and peoples planet wide
In village, or city massed.

Facing heat or facing cold,
Starving or replete,

Body you just soldiered on,
Surviving, on your feet.

So body, please now speak to me,
From your wisdom to survive,

From the countless ages of your time,
From death, from years alive.

What secrets do you hold within
Your pathways and your cells,

Your potions, miracles and genes,
Your sights and sounds and smells?

Teach me to blend with myriad time,
Upwards, sideways, down,

Teach me movement without end,
From bubbling well to crown.

Teach me merging, watching while
The laws of Nature trade

In what appears a compromise
With what the laws have made.

So on, and on, endeavouring
To speak a language true,

As antennae tongue attempts to tease
An old taste from a new.

So and on and back and forth,

Coming and going round,

Losing sense and finding sense
In words and wordless sound.

Body moves and body speaks out
Through the massed sensation.

Movement focusses meaning clear
Like countryside to station.

Mental fingers grasp at words
Old habits motion locking,

Do not give up, life whispers through
The past so blindly mocking.

There is a friend, a father
Calling faculty inborn,

Drawing threads together
Which the habits blindly scorn;

Seed arising from the earth,
Pushing up the shoots,

Yielding to bright sunlight
From the darkness of the roots.

MORE WORDS

What I have tried to do is show simple movements and a way of experiencing some of the potential impressions inherent in them... Sometimes, when someone is trying to do something, the teacher, friend or coach, looking on, will say,

"That's it, now you're really cooking."

So, the most important point in the Five Steps sequence is when you lower your foot from the raised position, to point A.

It is exactly at this point that you are tempted *not* to relax your front

leg, but on the contrary this is exactly when you *should* relax it. Keep the body weight on the rear leg, and when you are sure that the front one is relaxed, then, and only then, shift your weight forwards.

There is a fundamental principle underlying this movement and the way that it is performed. If you follow the suggestions in this book you will discover what it is, and benefit in a number of ways.

It may seem hard to credit that learning to move in a certain way can be helpful; more helpful in fact than reading many pages of inspirational and philosophical writing. The point is that moving in a certain way has an effect on the relationship between attention and the body which reading, in general, does not have.   Inspiration can help, but it is evanescent.   Words of philosphy mean one thing now, and something else an hour later. Forming a relationship between the attention and the body is much more substantial.

The values inherited from our educational system, and many of the things inherited from our western culture make it hard to credit this assertion. But do not take my word for it. Try it.

Five Steps sequence in full - 1

Fig. 1 - stand up straight and relax.

Fig. 2 - place foot and draw up ankle. Do not shift centre of gravity forwards.

Fig. 3 - Relax front leg and lower foot to ground. Do not shift centre of gravity forwards.

Fig. 4 - Incline body into a straight line, relaxing arms and chest.

1   2   3   4

Fig. 5 - bob up slowly like a weighted doll.

Fig. 6 - raise arms and leg simultaneously.

Fig. 7. - continue to raise arms and leg, turning elbows out.

Fig. 8 - thigh is horizontal and elbows begin to dip.

Fig. 9 - begin to lower arms and leg together.

When the left leg reaches the floor, place the heel down as the right foot shows in fig. 2 and begin the sequence over again.

5   6   7   8   9

Five Steps sequence in full - 2

1 - as you stand, be aware of the pull of gravity on your whole body.

2 - as you place your right heel, see if you can use only the muscles that are needed to do this.

3 - as you lower your right foot, be aware of the whole of the foot.

4 - vary the shift forwards sometimes by sitting down on your left leg, bending the trunk into line, and *then* shifting forwards into position 4.

1   2   3   4

5 - as you straighten up, imagine that you push a balloon up with your head.

6 - be aware of your chest as you begin this move, and the effects which accompany it.

7 - picture your arms as bird's wings and your leg making the step of a large long-legged bird.

8 - sometimes straighten up the small of your back as you reach position 8.

9 - imagine you are a water bird settling on to the water surface.

| 5 | 6 | 7 | 8 | 9 |

Five Steps sequence in full - 3

1 - as you stand, relax your hands: wrists, palms and fingers, right to the tips.

2 - as you place your right foot, be aware of the ankle, heel, sole and toes, right to the tips.

3 - lowering your right foot, glance down and make sure your left knee is in line with your left foot.

4 - relax your chest, shoulders and arms as you lean forwards. All the work is done by the back, let the front go.

1   2   3   4

5 - check that you are not holding your breath as you straighten.

6 - synchronise your leg raise with your arms raise - in concert.

7 - imagine your arms are "blown" up as if by air pressure from beneath.

8 - be observant of not pausing as you change from up to down; make a smooth changeover.

9 - because you are coming to the end of the sequence, do not let your attention fade.

| 5 | 6 | 7 | 8 | 9 |

Five Steps sequence in full - 4

1 - as you stand, relax your face

2 - notice what happens to your overall muscle state as you move for the first time.

3 - let the relaxation of the ankle and leg flow into your whole body.

4 - keep the gaze of your eyes at right angles to your trunk; don't let it wander up or sideways or down.

1   2   3   4

5 - notice the big change in the overall sensation of yourself as you straighten up into the vertical, "human" position.

6 - arms and leg "fly" but the supporting leg stays "grounded".

7 - sometimes "point" your elbows out to emphasise their movement.

8 - make sure you do not lean back from the vertical.

9 - get ready for the next sequence so that it does not take you by surprise.

5	6	7	8	9

Five Steps sequence in full - 5

1 - as you stand, sometimes relax your knees a little more to lower your centre of gravity.

2 - sometimes, as you place your your heel, circle your shoulders to loosen them more.

3 - sometimes, imagine that as you lower your foot you "plant" the supporting leg in the earth like a post.

4 - sometimes, imagine you glide forward into the lean position like an ice skater.

1   2   3   4

5 - it is not easy to allow the arms and shoulders to move back into a gravity hanging position, without assistance, as you straighten. Watch this.

6 - let your arms and leg move up very, very slowly, sometimes.

7 - sometimes, let your mind move ahead of your body, imagining that your arms and leg are already moving down before they are; this may help you to move smoothly in transition.

8 - check that both hands have a slightly curved shape.

9 - sometimes, but never make it a regular thing, stop completely at the end of the sequence for some seconds before continuing.

| 5 | 6 | 7 | 8 | 9 |

Five Steps sequence in full - 6

1 - occasionally, note the expression on your face as you stand. What is it? Is it necessary?

2 - sometimes, sense that your foot is blown gently off the ground as you lift it.

3 - as you lower your foot, sense that it is pressing down air.

4 - when you do this move, don't hold back and don't lunge forward.

| 1 | 2 | 3 | 4 |

5 - when you straighten up, are you holding your breath?

6 - when you raise your arms and leg, are you tensing unnecessary muscles?

7 - as you reach the upper limit of raising, make sure that you have a relaxed jaw.

8 - continue to relax your jaw as you start to come down.

9 - imagine you sink into water, up to your jaw, and your jaw floats in the water.

5   6   7   8   9

Five Steps sequence in full - 7

1 - sometimes stand still for five minutes before you start.

2 - sometimes stop in this position for a minute before going on.

3 - sometimes stop in this position for a minute before going on.

4 - sometimes stop in this position for ten seconds before going on.

1   2   3   4

5 - sometimes stop in this position for ten seconds before going on.

6 - sometimes stop in this position for ten seconds before going on.

7 - sometimes stop in this position for ten seconds before going on.

8/9 - sometimes let your arms and leg drop quickly, to disturb your concentration, so that you have to find it again. Do not injure your heel, so exert some control as it reaches the floor.

| 5 | 6 | 7 | 8 | 9 |

Five Steps sequence in full - 8

How many processes are taking place when you do the Five Steps?

They are so numerous that they cannot be counted.

Like Oliver Sachs' unusual patients, and like Dustin Hoffman's Rain Man, it would need another special "sense" or organ to be able to take them all in with one scan, however prolonged, and however deep.

This special scan, this special span, of attention, is what is undeveloped in all of us. It is safe to say in all of us because the numbers of people in whom it is developed must be so small as to be numerically negligble.

1	2	3	4

Though negligible in numbers, they are however, and have always been, far from negligible in influence. Otherwise we would all be living in unimaginable conditions.

If you work at the Five Steps along the lines indicated, it it my conviction that you will begin to develop a capacity in yourself which is seriously needed. It may be a capacity which someone once described as part of man's possible evolution.

AFTER-WORD WORDS...

If you have come this far and tried everything for some time, you have my congratulations and sympathy. Congratulations for persistence, and sympathy because I know from experience it is not easy. You may also have begun to wonder about your usually taken for granted modes of perception. The Five Steps open up new avenues of perception, mainly in relation to perceptions of the body, but not exclusively.

You must also have noticed how quickly and easily the state or mode of quiet concentration which the Five Steps can develop disappears? When you have stopped concentrating on or paying attention to the movements, a thought about something else will appear, or the phone will go, or someone will speak to you, and this new state or mood will vanish, or at best evaporate rapidly. Why is this?

A long, analytical explanation is out of place here, but using the vocabulary of this book we can say that your attention is absorbed by the new thought, phone call or voice of someone else. One moment you were focussed on your body and the next you are not. Why is this?

This was a question, framed with less understanding, that I myself had in my teenage years. Why do our moods or states change so quickly and so easily; so unresistingly and so unquestioningly? Why is this?

Another way of seeing this situation is to begin at the other end of the scale, so to speak, and ask why is there apparently nothing solid, nothing enduring, nothing firmly rooted in our make-up; a core from which we might live? Why is this?

It is a lack which many people feel, though it is formulated in a wide variety of ways. Just as I have suggested in this book that to understand the body better we need a special vocabulary, so to understand this lack also, we need a vocabulary based on observation and experience.

To arrive at this vocabulary we cannot use the words and ideas we have been brought up to use. Or rather, we cannot use them and attribute to them the meanings we have been brought up to use. These meanings have partly contributed to the condition in which we find ourselves, so there is no direct help from them.

To arrive at this vocabulary we need to give to some of the most common words we use a different meaning, to eliminate some of the most widespread ideas which we use and take for granted, and to find this different meaning from observation and experience. For this it seems inevitable to find someone who has done this already, and learn from him or her.

KEEPING STILL

Many people have tried sitting or standing still, today, and over the preceding centuries. It has been used by religious groups, martial arts students, followers of some form of yoga, various therapy systems and many others. Why?

Explanations vary. Some people say that when they are still they can come closer to God, or to a higher force, or to the flow of the chi or vital energy, or to a sense of being deeply centred in themselves... and so on.

Do the words matter very much? To some people they obviously do, because they relate what they experience in stillness to what they intellectually believe or to what their feelings respond.

But leaving words of belief behind, and reducing the practise to its simplest, keeping still is surely a necessary part of normal life? Nature obliges us to keep relatively still by making us sleep, every night. This is involuntary. We have to sleep, otherwise we would die or go mad. Since wise Nature compels us to become still in sleep, why not take this as a lesson and keep still for a while, voluntarily, during our waking day?

The Five Steps suggests this, prior to beginning to move. But in addition to the times when you train at the Five Steps, why not sit still each day, for a time, and give everything a rest?

In doing so, you will not only automatically benefit, but will begin to see things about yourself which are not so apparent when you are moving. In general, this is good advice.

If you have seriously tried to follow the contents of the book and have emerged with questions which matter to you, write to the author:

Paul Crompton
94 Felsham Road, London, sw15 1dq, England.